Table of Contents

Medical and Applied Sciences

Dr. Evelyn J. Biluk

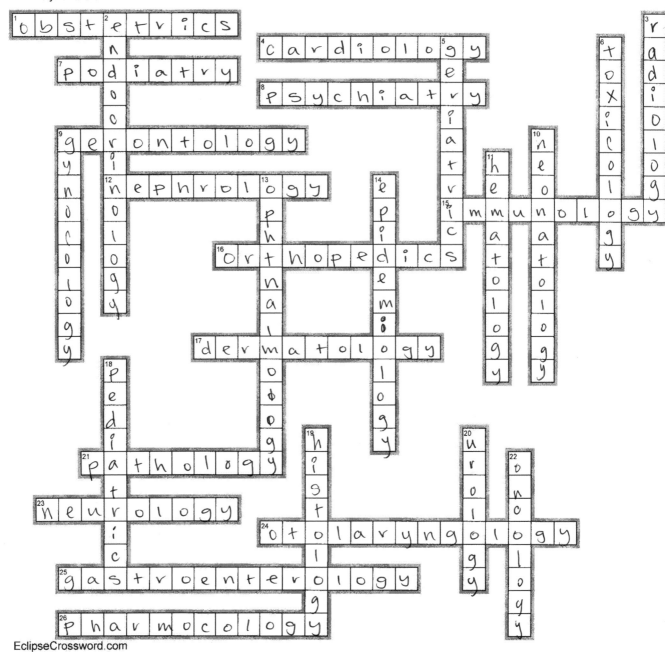

Medical and Applied Sciences

Dr. Evelyn J. Biluk

Across

1. Branch of medicine involved with pregnancy and childbirth
4. Branch of medical science dealing with the heart and heart diseases
7. Study of the care and treatment of feet
8. Branch of medicine dealing with the mind and associated disorders
9. Study of the aging process and the problems of older individuals
12. Study of kidneys and associated diseases
15. Study of body's resistance to disease
16. Branch of medicine dealing with muscular and skeletal systems and their associated problems
17. Study of skin and its diseases
21. Study of the changes within the body associated with disease
23. Study of nervous system health and disease
✗ 24. Study of the ears, throat, larynx and their associated diseases   _otolaryngology_
25. Study of the stomach and intestines and their associated diseases
26. Study of drugs and their use in treatment of diseases

Down

2. Study of hormones and associated diseases
3. Study of Xrays and their uses in diagnosing and treating diseases
✗ 5. Branch of medicine dealing with older people and their medical problems   _geriatrics_ vs gerontology
6. Study of poisonous substances and the effects of physiology
9. Study of female reproductive system and its diseases
✗ 10. Study of newborns and treatment of newborn disorders   neonatology
11. Study of blood and blood diseases
✗ 13. Study of the eyes and eye diseases   ophthalmology
✗ 14. Study of the factors that contribute to determining the spread and frequency of health-related conditions within a specific human population   epidemiology
18. Branch of medicine dealing with children and the related diseases
19. Study of tissues (microscopic anatomy only)
20. Branch of medicine dealing with urinary and male reproductive systems and their associated

diseases
22. Study of cancers

Medical and Applied Sciences

Dr. Evelyn J. Biluk

Word bank

CARDIOLOGY   DERMATOLOGY   ENDOCRINOLOGY   EPIDEMIOLOGY   GASTROENTEROLOGY

GERIATRICS   GERONTOLOGY   GYNECOLOGY   HEMATOLOGY   HISTOLOGY   IMMUNOLOGY

NEONATOLOGY   NEPHROLOGY   NEUROLOGY   OBSTETRICS   ONCOLOGY   OPHTHALMOLOGY

ORTHOPEDICS   OTOLARYNGOLOGY   PATHOLOGY   PEDIATRICS   PHARMACOLOGY   PODIATRY

PSYCHIATRY   RADIOLOGY   TOXICOLOGY   UROLOGY

Medical and Applied Sciences

Dr. Evelyn J. Biluk

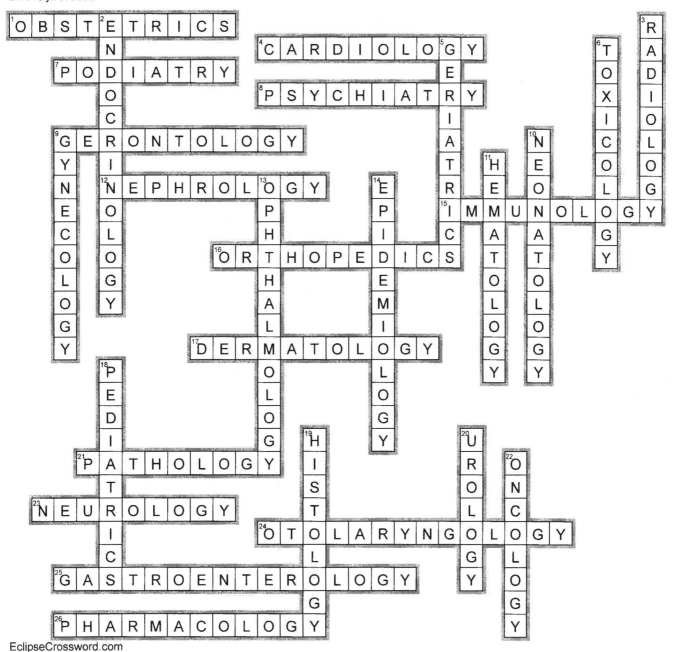

Levels of Structural Organization and Body Systems

Dr. Evelyn J. Biluk

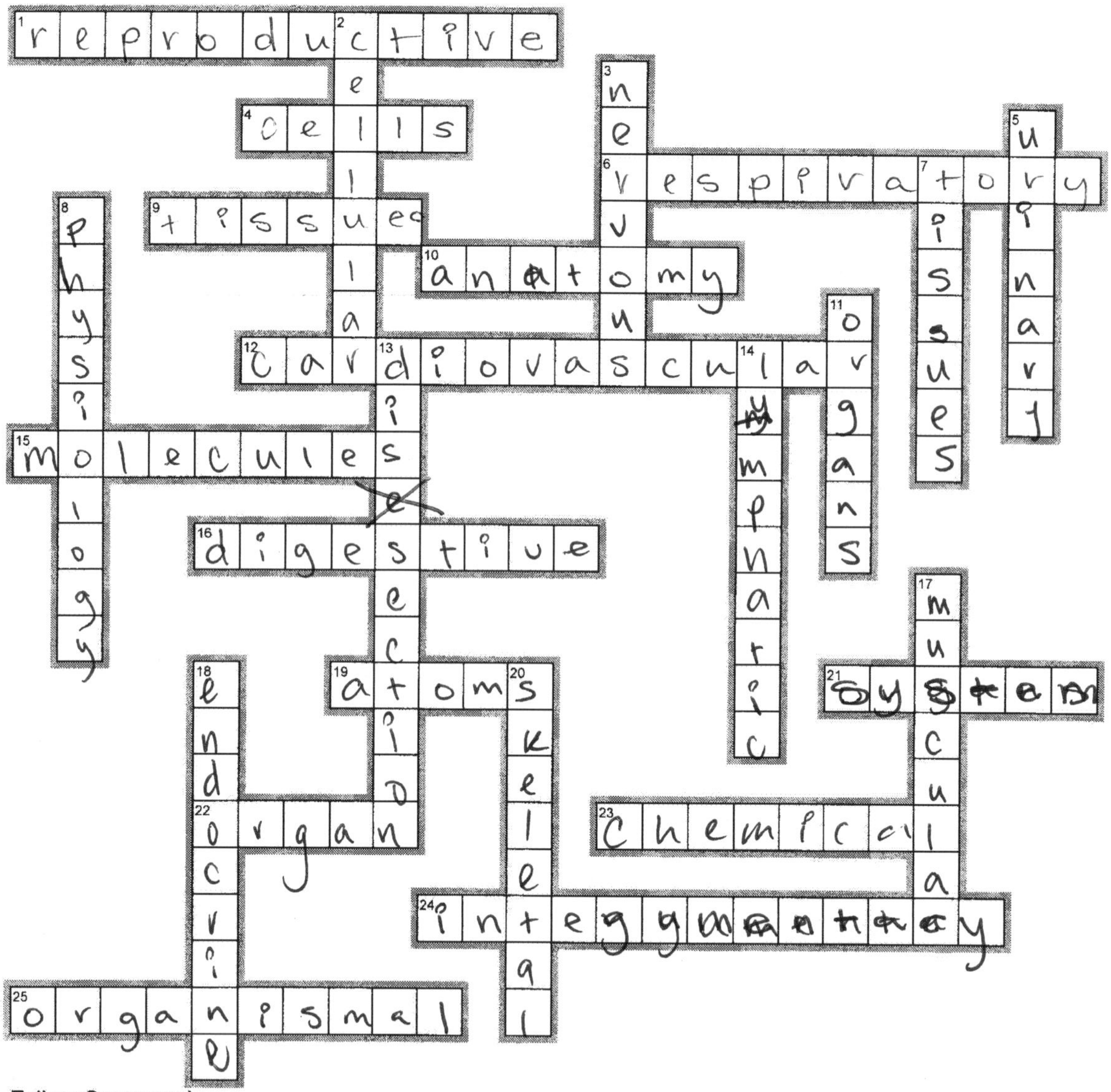
1 reproductive
2 cellular
3 nervous
4 cells
5 urinary
6 respiratory
7 tissues
8 physiology
9 tissue
10 anatomy
11 organs
12 cardiovascular
13 dissection
14 lymphatic
15 molecules
16 digestive
17 muscular
18 endocrine
19 atoms
20 skeletal
21 system
22 organ
23 chemical
24 integumentary
25 organismal

Levels of Structural Organization and Body Systems

Dr. Evelyn J. Biluk

Across

1. Includes testes (males) and ovaries (females); Uterine tubes, uterus and vagina (female); Epididymis, ductus deferens and penis (males)

4. Basic structural and functional units of an organism

6. This system transports oxygen from inhaled air to blood and carbon dioxide from blood to exhaled air; Regulates acid-base balance of body fluids; Produces sounds

9. Level contains tissues only (epithelial, connective, muscular and nervous)

10. Science of body structures and the relationships among them   *anatomy*

12. The blood, heart and blood vessels are a part of this system

15. Two or more atoms jointed together

16. The _____ system includes organs of GI tract

19. Smallest units of matter that participate in chemical reactions

21. This level includes systems of the body (digestive, respiratory, integumentary, etc ...)

22. This level includes organs (stomach, skin, bones, heart, liver, lungs, brain)

23. This level contains atoms and molecules

24. This system includes the skin, hair, nails, sweat glands and oil glands

25. This level includes the organism

20. This system includes bones and joints of the body and their associated cartilages

Down

2. This level includes cells

3. The _____ system includes the brain, spinal cord, nerves, and special sense organs

5. The kidneys, ureters, bladder and urethra are part of this system

7. Groups of cells that work together to perform a particular function

8. Science of body functions

11. Structures that are composed of two or more different types of tissues that have specific functions

13. Cutting apart of body structures to study their relationships

14. This system returns proteins and fluid to the blood; Carries lipids from GI tract to blood; Protects the body against disease-causing microbes

17. The _____ system is composed of muscles

18. This system includes hormone-producing glands and hormone-producing cells

Levels of Structural Organization and Body Systems

Dr. Evelyn J. Biluk

Word bank

ANATOMY   ATOMS   CARDIOVASCULAR   CELLS   CELLULAR   CHEMICAL   DIGESTIVE

DISSSECTION   ENDOCRINE   INTEGUMENTARY   LYMPHATIC   MOLECULES   MUSCULAR   NERVOUS

ORGAN   ORGANISMAL   ORGANS   PHYSIOLOGY   REPRODUCTIVE   RESPIRATORY   SKELETAL

SYSTEM   TISSUE   TISSUES   URINARY

Levels of Structural Organization and Body Systems

Dr. Evelyn J. Biluk

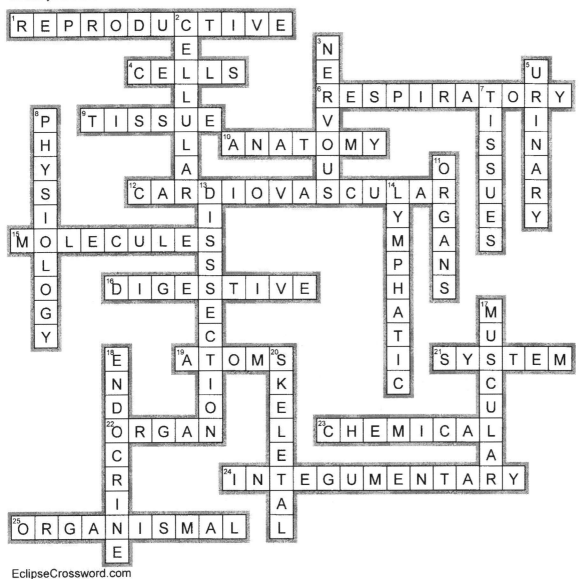

Anterior and Posterior Body Regions

Dr. Evelyn J. Biluk

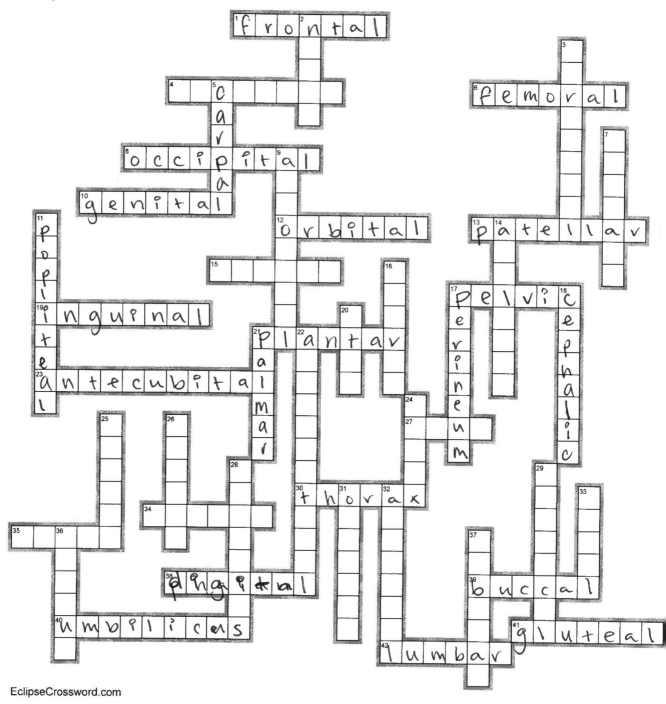

1. frontal
4. (blank) — 5 down: carpal
6. femoral
8. occipital
10. genital
12. orbital
13. patellar
17. pelvic
19. inguinal
21. plantar
21 down: palmar
23. antecubital
30. thorax
17 down: perineum
18 down: cephalic
38. digital
39. buccal
40. umbilicus
41. gluteal
42. lumbar
11. popliteal

Anterior and Posterior Body Regions

Dr. Evelyn J. Biluk

Across

1. Forehead
4. Chest
6. Thigh
8. Lower posterior region of head
10. Reproductive organs (male/female)
12. Eye cavity
13. Front of knee
15. Abdomen
17. Pelvis
19. Depressed area of abdominal wall near thigh (groin)
21. Sole of foot
23. Space in front of elbow
27. Mouth
30. Ribs
34. Instep of foot (ankle)
35. Foot
38. Fingers or toes
39. Cheek
40. Navel
41. Buttocks
42. Lower back (between ribs and pelvis)

Down

2. Nose
3. Spinal column
5. Wrist
7. Breast
9. Region between pelvis and thorax
11. Behind knee
14. Arm pit
16. Leg
17. Region between external reproductive organs and anus
18. head
20. Ear
21. Palm of hand
22. Forearm
24. Hip
25. Posterior region between hip bones

26. Chin
28. Arm
29. Neck
31. Anterior middle thorax
32. Point of shoulder
33. Leg calf
36. Back
37. Elbow

Anterior and Posterior Body Regions

Dr. Evelyn J. Biluk

Word bank

ABDOMINAL   ACROMIAL   ANTEBRACHIAL   ANTECUBITAL   AXILLARY   BRACHIAL   BUCCAL

CARPAL   CELIAC   CEPHALIC   CERVICAL   COSTAL   COXAL   CRURAL   CUBITAL   DIGITAL

DORSUM   FEMORAL   FRONTAL   GENITAL   GLUTEAL   INGUINAL   LUMBAR   MAMMARY

MENTAL   NASAL   OCCIPITAL   ORAL   ORBITAL   OTIC   PALMAR   PATELLAR   PECTORAL

PEDAL   PELVIC   PERINEAL   PLANTAR   POPLITEAL   SACRAL   STERNAL   SURAL   TARSAL

UMBILICAL   VERTEBRAL

Anterior and Posterior Body Regions

Dr. Evelyn J. Biluk

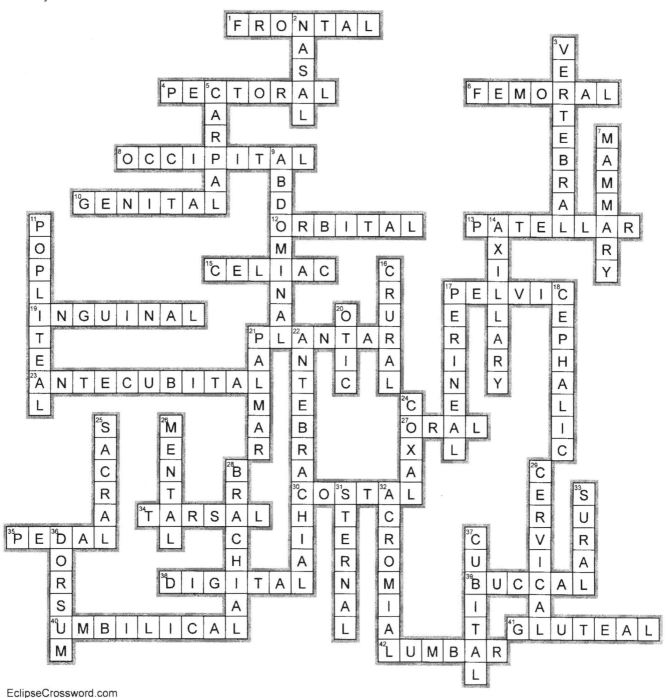

Directional Terms, Planes and Body Cavities

Dr. Evelyn J. Biluk

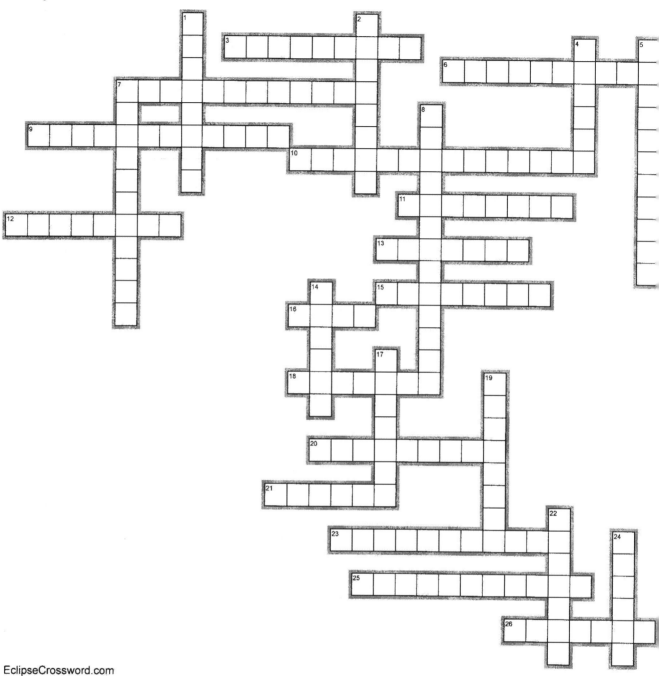

EclipseCrossword.com

Directional Terms, Planes and Body Cavities

Dr. Evelyn J. Biluk

Across

3. Cavity that contains the stomach, spleen, liver, gallbladder, small intestine and most of the large intestine

6. Plane that divides the body or an organ into superior and inferior portions; Also called cross-sectional or horizontal

7. Between two structures

9. Vertical plane that divides the body or an organ into unequal right or left sides

10. Cavity subdivided into abdominal and pelvic cavities

11. Nearer to the attachment of a limb to the trunk

12. Vertical plane that divides the body or an organ into right and left sides

13. Plane that passes through the body or an organ at an angle between a transverse plane and sagittal plane or between a transverse plane and a frontal plane

15. Nearer to or at the front of the body

16. Away from the surface of the body

18. Farther from the midline

20. Nearer to or at the back of the body

21. Nearer to the midline

23. Toward or on the surface of the body

25. Region in the central portion of the thoracic cavity

26. Cavity formed by cranial bones and contains the brain

Down

1. Toward the head

2. Away from the head

4. Cavity contains bladder, portion of large intestine and internal reproductive organs

5. Cavity surrounds the heart

7. On the same side of the body as another structure

8. On the opposite side of the body from another structure

14. Vertical plane through the midline of the body or an organ and divides it into equal right and left sides; Also called midsagittal

17. Plane divides the body or an organ into anterior and posterior portions; Also called coronal

19. Chest cavity; Contains pleural cavity, pericardial cavity and mediastinum

22. Cavity surrounds a lung

24. Farther from the point of attachment of a limb to the trunk

Directional Terms, Planes and Body Cavities

Dr. Evelyn J. Biluk

Word bank

ABDOMINAL   ABDOMINOPELVIC   ANTERIOR   CONTRALATERAL   CRANIAL   DEEP   DISTAL

FRONTAL   INFERIOR   INTERMEDIATE   IPSILATERAL   LATERAL   MEDIAL   MEDIAN   MEDIASTINUM

OBLIQUE   PARASAGITTAL   PELVIC   PERICARDIAL   PLEURAL   POSTERIOR   PROXIMAL

SAGITTAL   SUPERFICIAL   SUPERIOR   THORACIC   TRANSVERSE

Directional Terms, Planes and Body Cavities

Dr. Evelyn J. Biluk

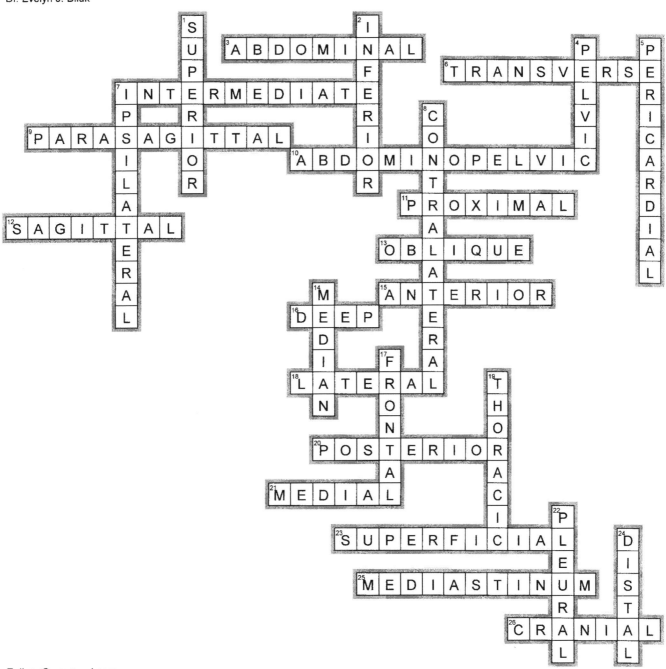

Chemical Bonds and Chemical Reactions

Dr. Evelyn J. Biluk

Chemical Bonds and Chemical Reactions

Dr. Evelyn J. Biluk

Across

1. The initial energy investment needed to start a chemical reaction

3. _____ reactions need energy

4. Also known as stored energy

5. Forces of attraction that hold atoms together

9. The capacity to do work

11. _____ reactions have end products that can revert to the original reactants

12. Synthesis reactions are _____

15. _____ reactions involve breaking down a substance into smaller (simpler) molecules

16. The ending substances of a chemical reaction are called _____

19. Decomposition reactions are _____

22. This molecule couples both endergonic and exergonic reactions

23. Sum total of protons and neutrons of an atom

24. Formed by two atoms sharing electrons

25. Positively charged ion

26. Same number of protons but different number of neutrons for an element

27. _____ bond occurs when the force of attraction between ions of opposite charge holds them together

28. A _____ bond forms between a hydrogen atom and an oxygen atom (or a nitrogen atom)

19. These molecules accelerate chemical reactions

20. _____ reactions involve the combination of reactions to make larger (complex) molecules

21. Contains atoms of two or more elements

Down

1. Number of protons

2. Chemical bonds result from gaining, losing or sharing _____

6. _____ reactions release energy

7. Electrically charged atom or group of atoms with an unpaired electron in its outermost shell

8. Atoms become stable with 8 electrons in their _____

10. _____ reactions involve replacing one atom or atoms by another atom or atoms

13. Negative charged ion

14. _____ bond occurs when atoms share pairs of valence electrons

17. Also known as the energy of motion

18. The starting substances in a chemical reaction are called _____

Chemical Bonds and Chemical Reactions

Dr. Evelyn J. Biluk

Word bank

ACTIVATIONENERGY   ANABOLIC   ANION   ATOMICMASS   ATOMICNUMBER   ATP   CATABOLIC

CATALYSTS   CATION   CHEMICALBONDS   COMPOUND   COVALENT   DECOMPOSITION   ELECTRONS

ENDERGONIC   ENERGY   EXCHANGE   EXERGONIC   FREERADICAL   HYDROGEN   IONIC

ISOTOPES   KINETICENERGY   MOLECULE   POTENTIALENERGY   PRODUCTS   REACTANTS

REVERSIBLE   SYNTHESIS   VALENCESHELL

Chemical Bonds and Chemical Reactions

Dr. Evelyn J. Biluk

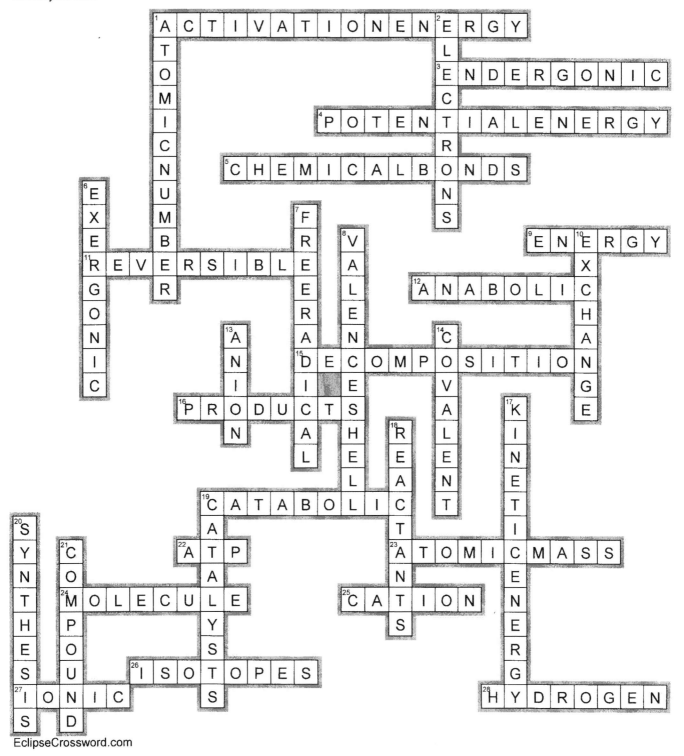

EclipseCrossword.com

Macromolecules

Dr. Evelyn J. Biluk

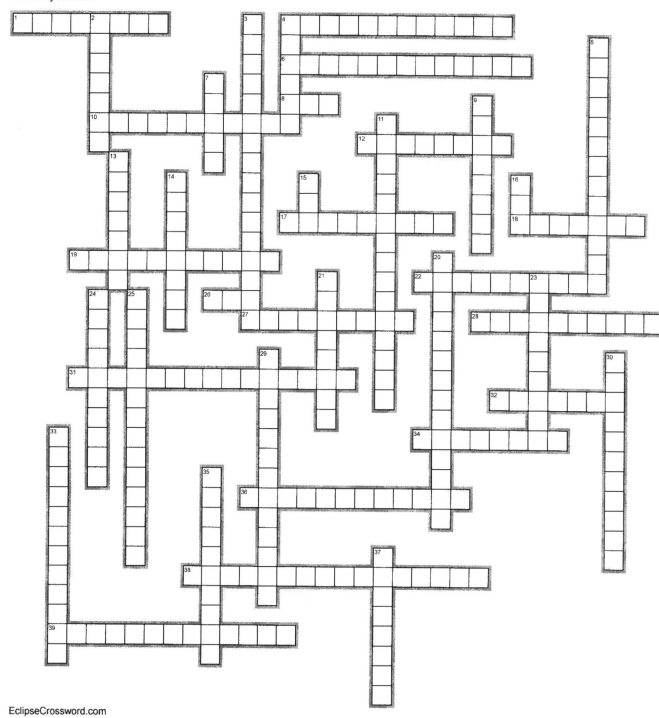

Macromolecules

Dr. Evelyn J. Biluk

Across

1. Large molecules containing carbon, hydrogen, oxygen, nitrogen and sometimes sulfur

4. Lipid/protein complex

6. This lipid makes up most of the membrane that surrounds each cell

8. AKA deoxyribonucleic acid

10. Group includes prostaglandins and leukotrienes

12. Large molecule formed by the covalent bonding of many idential or similar monomers

17. _____ fatty acid contains a single covalent bond between the carbond atoms of the hydrocarbon chain

18. _____ structure is a sequence of amino acids linked by peptide bonds to form a polypeptide chain

19. A chain of carbons bonded to hydrogen atoms

22. Simplest lipid; Used to make triglycerides and phospholipids

26. AKA adenosine triphosphate; Energy of living systems

27. _____ structure is the repeated twisting or folding of neighboring amino acids in a polypeptide chain

28. Pentose sugar, phosphate group and nitrogenous base

31. Contain 3 to 7 carbon atoms; Known as the simple sugars; Example is glucose

32. Molecules having the same molecular formula but different structures

34. Main polysaccharide in human body

36. Protein loses its shape due to changes in its environment

38. RNA takes part in _____

39. Combination of two monosaccharides by dehydration synthesis; Example is sucrose

11. Contains tens or hundreds of monosaccharides joined through dehydration synthesis; Example is glycogen

13. _____ bond is a covalent bond that joins each pair of amino acids in a protein

14. Polysaccharides formed from glucose by plants

15. AKA ribonucleic acid

16. ATP is made from _____ and a phosphate group

20. Chain of carbon atoms in an organic molecule

21. Small building block molecules

23. Polysaccharide formed from glucose by plants that cannot be digested by humans

24. Monomers of proteins

25. Very large molecules composed of polymers

29. Most plentiful lipid in your diet

30. _____ fatty acid contains one or more double covalent bonds between the carbon atoms of the hydrocarbon chain

33. Huge organic molecules that contain carbon, hydrogen, oxygen, nitrogen and phosphorus

35. _____ structure is the arrangement of polypeptide chains relative to each other

37. Cholesterol is an example of this lipid group; Four rings of carbon atoms

Down

2. Protein molecules that function as catalysts

3. Other atoms or molecules bound to the hydrocarbon skeleton

4. Contain carbon, hydrogen and oxygen; Insoluble in polar solvents like water; Includes fatty acids, triglycerides, phospholipids, steroids and eicosanoids

5. Includes sugars, glycogen, starches and cellulose

7. DNA is the primary chemical in _____

9. _____ structure is the 3D shape of a polypeptide chain

Macromolecules

Dr. Evelyn J. Biluk

Word bank

ADP   AMINOACIDS   ATP   CARBOHYDRATES   CARBONSKELETON   CELLULOSE   DENATURATION

DISACCHARIDES   DNA   EICOSANOIDS   ENZYMES   FATTYACIDS   FUNCTIONALGROUPS   GENES

GLYCOGEN   HYDROCARBON   ISOMERS   LIPIDS   LIPOPROTEINS   MACROMOLECULES

MONOMERS   MONOSACCHARIDES   NUCLEICACIDS   NUCLEOTIDE   PEPTIDE   PHOSPHOLIPIDS

POLYMERS   POLYSACCHARIDES   PRIMARY   PROTEINS   PROTEINSYNTHESIS   QUATERNARY   RNA

SATURATED   SECONDARY   STARCHES   STEROIDS   TERTIARY   TRIGLYCERIDES

UNSATURATED

Macromolecules

Dr. Evelyn J. Biluk

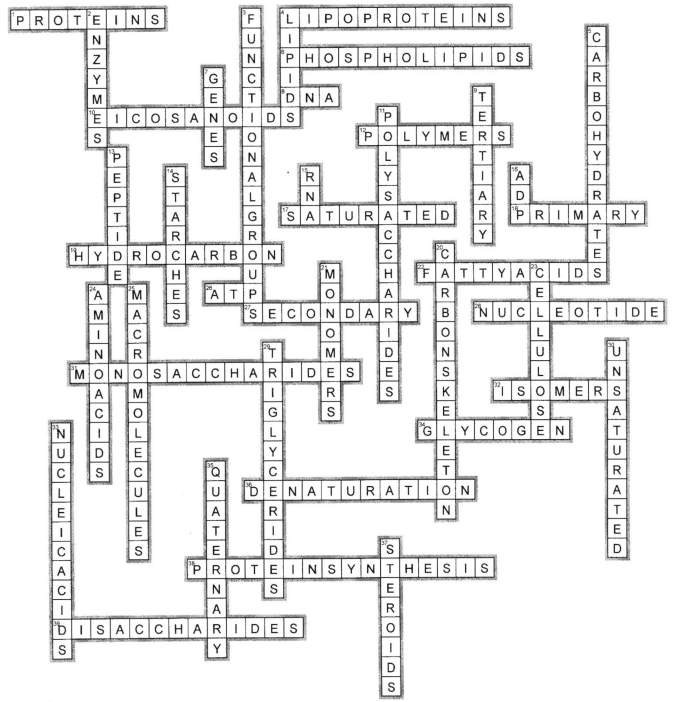

EclipseCrossword.com

Cell Parts

Dr. Evelyn J. Biluk

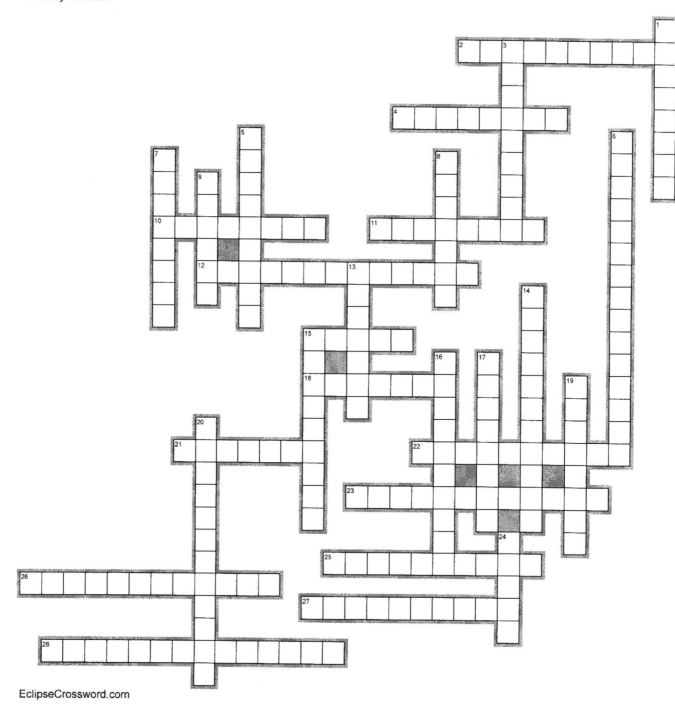

Cell Parts

Dr. Evelyn J. Biluk

Across

2. Nonmotile microscopic fingerlike projection of cell membrane

4. One or more spherical bodies inside the nucleus that produce ribosomes

10. The study of relationships between the genome and the biological functions of an organism

11. Vesicle formed from Golgi complex; Contains digestive enzymes

12. Site of aerobic cellular respiration reactions (produce most of the cell's energy - ATP)

15. Structure moves fluids over a cell's surface

18. Membranous network of flattened sacs or tubules covered by ribosomes

21. Repeated sequences of the human genome that do not code for proteins

22. Pair of centrioles and pericentriolar material

23. Network of microfilaments, intermediate filaments and microtubules

25. Specialized structures with characteristic shapes and functions

26. Modifies glycoproteins, glycolipids and lipoproteins, then sorts and packages them for transport

27. Vesicle that contains oxidases and catalase

28. Protects cellular contents; Makes contact with other cells; Contains channels, transporters, enzymes, cell identity markers and linker proteins

16. Tiny barrel shaped structure that contains proteases

17. Membranous network of flattened sacs or tubules that lack ribosomes

19. Composed of rRNA and proteins

20. Openings that extend throughout the nuclear envelope

24. Cell's hereditary units

Down

1. DNA wrapped twice around a core of 8 proteins

3. Cellular contents between plasma membrane and nucleus

5. Complex of DNA, proteins, and some RNA

6. Double membrane that separates the nucleus from the cytoplasm

7. Structure moves an entire cell

8. Medium in which many of a cell's metabolic reactions occur

9. Total genetic info carries in a cell or within an organism

13. Spherical shaped structure that is most prominent feature of a cell; Contains chromosomes and nucleolus

14. Genes are arranged along _____; Humans have 46 of these (23 from each parent)

15. One copy of duplicated DNA making up a chromosome

Cell Parts

Dr. Evelyn J. Biluk

Word bank

CENTROSOME   CHROMATID   CHROMATIN   CHROMOSOMES   CILIA   CYTOPLASM   CYTOSKELETON

CYTOSOL   FLAGELLA   GENES   GENOME   GENOMICS   GOLGICOMPLEX   HISTONES

JUNKDNA   LYSOSOME   MICROVILLI   MITOCHONDRION   NUCLEARENVELOPE   NUCLEARPORES

NUCLEOLI   NUCLEUS   ORGANELLES   PEROXISOME   PLASMAMEMBRANE   PROTEASOME

RIBOSOME   ROUGHER   SMOOTHER

Cell Parts

Dr. Evelyn J. Biluk

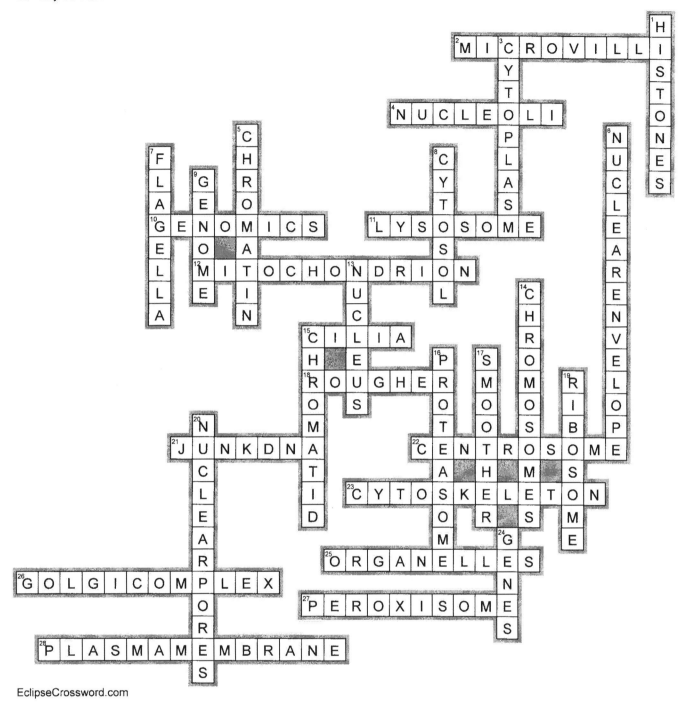

EclipseCrossword.com

Cell Division
Dr. Evelyn J. Biluk

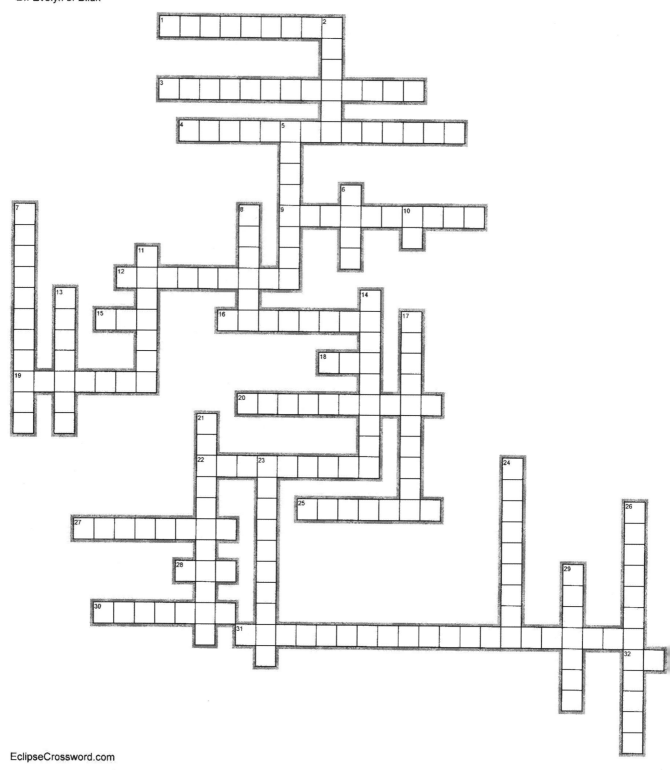

Cell Division
Dr. Evelyn J. Biluk

Across

1. Normal type of cell death

3. Process that restores the diploid number of chromosomes after meiosis

4. Slight indentation of the plasma membrane start beings in late anaphase and ends after telophase

9. _____ chromosomes are the two chromosomes that make up each pair

12. The orderly sequence of events in which a somatic cell duplicated its contents and then divides into two cells

15. Meiosis consists of _____ successive stages

16. First stage of mitosis

18. _____ replicates during the S phase

19. The distribution of two sets of chromosomes into two separate nuclei

20. Cell does most of its growing during this phase; Includes G1, S and G2

22. Chromosomes resume chromatin form; Nuclear envelopes and nucleoli reappear; Opposite of prophase

25. _____ cells contain two sets of chromosomes

27. Pathological type of cell death resulting from tissue injury

28. _____ chromsomes are a single pair of chromosomes designating gender (X or Y)

30. Gametes contain one set of 23 chromosomes

31. Formation of new combination of genes

32. Cells remaining in G1 phase for a very long time and never destined to divide again are in this phase

14. During this stage, the chromosomes line up at the equatorial plate

17. Two haploid cells divide to form four haploid cells during this sexual reproductive stage

21. Cytoplasmic division

23. _____ are duplicated during the G1 phase

24. The net result of this sexual reproductive stage is two haploid cells that are genetically unlike each other

26. Exchange between parts of nonsister chromatids during Meiosis I

29. Enzyme and _____ synthesis continue during G2

Down

2. The interval between G1 and G2; Lasts only 8 hours

5. The centromere split and the two members of each chromatid pair separate and move towards opposite poles of the cell

6. The number of cells produced by meiosis

7. During prophase, chromatin fibers condense and shorten into _____

8. Uncontrolled cell division

10. Interval between mitotic phase and the S phase

11. Reproductive cell division that occurs in ovaries and testes

13. The _____ phase consists of mitosis and cytokinesis

Cell Division

Dr. Evelyn J. Biluk

Word bank

ANAPHASE   APOPTOSIS   CANCER   CELLCYCLE   CHROMOSOMES   CLEAVAGEFURROW
CROSSINGOVER   CYTOKINESIS   DIPLOID   DNA   FERTILIZATION   FOUR   G0   G1
GENETICRECOMBINATION   HAPLOID   HOMOLOGOUS   INTERPHASE   MEIOSIS   MEIOSIS I   MEIOSIS
II   METAPHASE   MITOSIS   MITOTIC   NECROSIS   ORGANELLES   PROPHASE   PROTEIN   SEX
SPHASE   TELOPHASE   TWO

Cell Division
Dr. Evelyn J. Biluk

Transport Processes

Dr. Evelyn J. Biluk

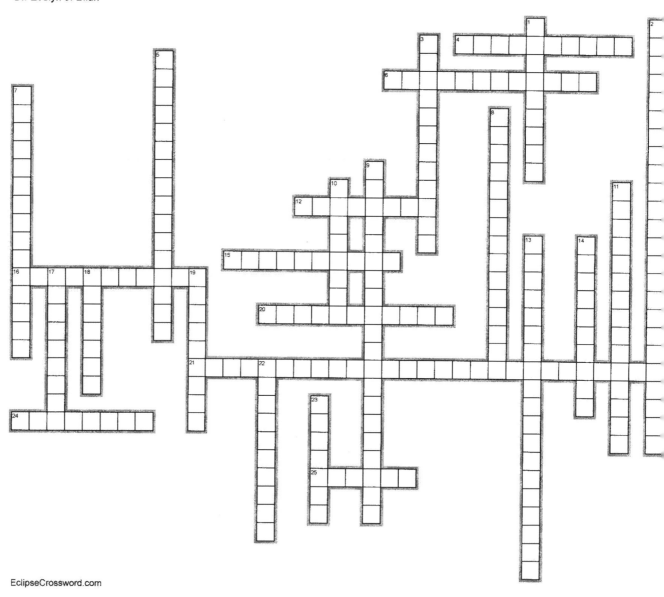

Transport Processes
Dr. Evelyn J. Biluk

Across

4. Vesicular transport; Moving materials out of a cell by the vesicle fusing with the plasma membrane and releasing the contents

6. Active process; Vesicles are used to transport substances into, across and out of a given cell

12. Tiny, spherical membrane sacs used to transport substances entering and/or leaving cells

15. _____ solution has a high concentration of solutes in comparison to the cytosol of RBCs; Cells will shrink (crenation)

16. Vesicular transport; Materials move into a cell using a vesicle that developed from the plasma membrane

20. Form of endocytosis; Tiny droplets of extracellular fluid are taken up by the cell

21. Type of endocytosis; Cells take up specific ligands; Vesicle forms after a receptor protein (found in plasma membrane) recognizes and binds to a particular particle in the extracellular fluid

24. Measure of a solution's ability to change the volume of cells by changing the water content

25. Also known as 0.9% NaCl; Isotonic solution used in healthcare

Down

1. _____ solution has a low concentration of solutes in comparison to the cytosol of RBCs; RBCs will swell and burst (hemolysis)

2. Using the energy stored in sodium ion or hydrogen ion concentration gradients to drive other substances across the plasma membrane against their own concentration gradients

3. Form of endocytosis; Cell engulfs large sold particles (e.g. viruses, bacteria)

5. One classification of cellular membrane transport; Does not require energy; Moves down the concentration gradient

7. Another classification of cellular membrane transport; Does require energy; Moves against the concentration gradient

8. Passive process; Substances move freely through the plasma membrane lipid bilayer without the assistance of transport proteins

9. Membrane protein assists a specific substance to cross the plasma membrane; Passive process

10. _____ solution has equal concentrations of solutes on both sides of the membrane in solution

11. Active process that requires energy to move substances across the membrane but against the concentration gradient

13. Most prevalent primary active transport mechanism; Expels sodium ions from cells; Brings in potassium ions

14. Transporters moving two substances in opposite directions across the plasma membrane

17. Passive process; Random mixing of particles in a solution because of its kinetic energy

18. Also known as a transporter

19. Transporters moving two substances in the same direction across the plasma membrane

22. Projections of the plasma membrane and cytoplasm used during phagocytosis

23. Type of diffusion; Passive process; Movement of a solvent through the plasma membrane; Movement of water (in living systems)

Transport Processes

Dr. Evelyn J. Biluk

Word bank

ACTIVEPROCESSES   ACTIVETRANSPORT   ANTIPORTER   CARRIER   DIFFUSION   ENDOCYTOSIS

EXOCYTOSIS   FACILITATEDDIFFUSION   HYPERTONIC   HYPOTONIC   ISOTONIC   OSMOSIS

PASSIVEPROCESSES   PHAGOCYTOSIS   PINOCYTOSIS   PSEUDOPODS

RECEPTORMEDIATEDENDOCYTOSIS   SALINE   SECONDARYACTIVETRANSPORT   SIMPLEDIFFUSION

SODIUMPOTASSIUMPUMP   SYMPORTER   TONICITY   TRANSCYTOSIS   VESICLES

Transport Processes

Dr. Evelyn J. Biluk

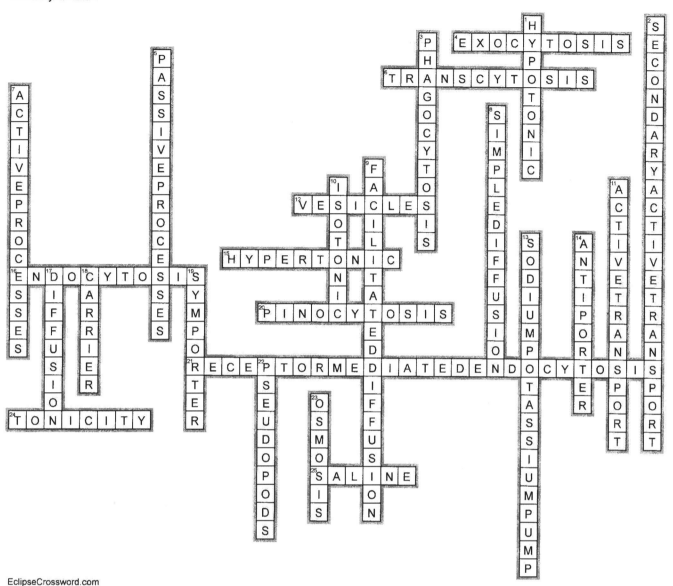

EclipseCrossword.com

Protein Synthesis

Dr. Evelyn J. Biluk

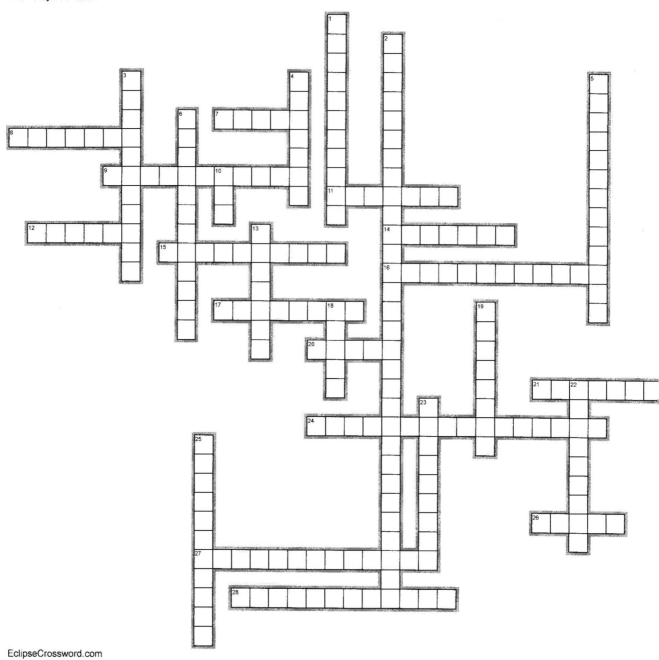

Protein Synthesis

Dr. Evelyn J. Biluk

Across

7. One of two binding sites on mRNA; Holds the next tRNA bearing its amino acid

8. Also abbreviated as "T"; Nitrogenous base found in DNA

9. Second stage of protein synthesis; Info contained in RNA is used to make of sequence of amino acids that form a new protein

11. Transcription takes place in the _____

12. Also abbreviated as "U"; Nitrogenous base found in RNA

14. Also abbreviated as "A"; Nitrogenous base found in DNA

15. DNA transcription stops at this nucleotide sequence

16. Also known as rRNA; Joins with ribosomal proteins to make ribosomes

17. Piece of DNA where transcription starts

20. Each DNA base triplet is transcribed into a complementary sequence of three nucleotides called a _____

21. Also abbreviated as "G"; Nitrogenous base found in DNA

24. Process of making proteins that the cell needs; Proteins are part of the cell membrane, cytoskeleton, other organelles, enzymes, transporters, etc ...

26. One of two binding sites on tRNA; First tRNA with a specific amino acid attaches to mRNA

27. First stage of protein synthesis; DNA is copied to produce RNA

28. Several ribosomes attached to the same mRNA

18. Pieces of DNA that do code for proteins

19. Also abbreviated as "C"; Nitrogenous base in DNA

22. One of an end of a tRNA carries a specific _____

23. The other end of a tRNA carries an _____ (nucleotide triplet)

25. DNA stores genetic info as a set of three _____

Down

1. Also known as tRNA; Binds to an amino acid and holds it in place on a ribosomes until it becomes part of the new protein being made

2. Enzymes that cut introns and splice together the exons; Also known as "snurps"

3. The sequence of three nucleotides in a DNA is called a

4. Transcript that contains introns and exons from transcription

5. Enzymes that catalyzes the transcription of DNA

6. Also known as mRNA; Directs the synthesis of a protein

10. Start codon on mRNA

13. Pieces of DNA that do not code for proteins

Protein Synthesis

Dr. Evelyn J. Biluk

Word bank

ADENINE   AMINOACID   ANTICODON   ASITE   AUG   BASETRIPLET   CODON   CYTOSINE   EXONS

GUANINE   INTRONS   MESSENGERRNA   NUCLEOTIDES   NUCLEUS   POLYRIBOSOME   PREMRNA

PROMOTER   PROTEINSYNTHESIS   PSITE   RIBOSOMALRNA   RNAPOLYMERASE

SMALLNUCLEARRIBONUCLEOPROTEINS   TERMINATOR   THYMINE   TRANSCRIPTION   TRANSFERRNA

TRANSLATION   URACIL

Protein Synthesis

Dr. Evelyn J. Biluk

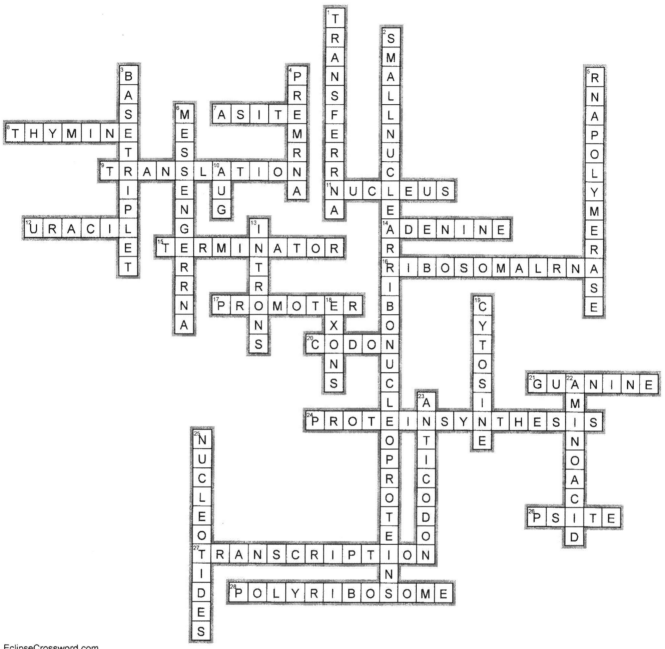

Epithelial Tissue

Dr. Evelyn J. Biluk

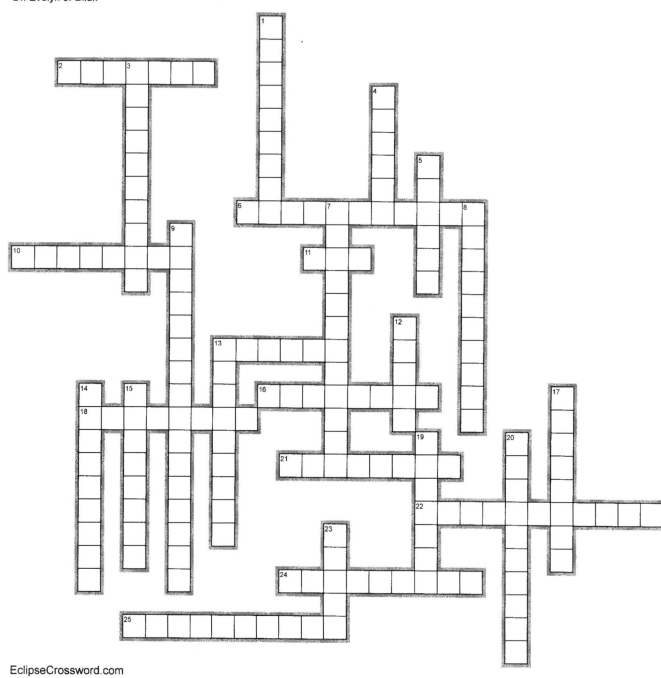

Epithelial Tissue
Dr. Evelyn J. Biluk

Across

2. Tough fibrous protein that helps protect the skin and underlying tissues

6. Epithelial layer of serous membranes (e.g. pericardium)

10. Thin, flat cells

11. This test involves the collection and examination of epithelial cells from the vagina and cervix

13. _____ cells secrete mucus; Associated with columnar epithelial cells

16. Cells shaped like cubes or hexagons

18. _____ glands secrete their products into ducts that empty onto the surface of a covering and lining epithelium or the lumen of a hollow organ

21. Cells that are taller than they are wider; Like columns

22. Single squamous epithelium that lines the heart, blood vessels and lymphatic vessels

24. Epithelial tissue is _____ (lacks a blood supply)

25. _____ epithelium consists of two or more layers of cells

Down

1. _____ glands secrete hormones into the interstitial fluid and then they diffuse into the bloodstream

3. Intake of fluids or other substances (e.g., digested food)

4. _____ epithelium is a single layer of cells

5. This free surface of an epithelial cell faces the body surface, body cavity, lumen of an internal organ or a duct that receives cell secretions

7. Cells that change shape; From flat to cuboidal and back

8. Finger like projections that increase the surface area of the cell membrane

9. _____ epithelium is a simple epithelium; Does not consist of multiple layers

12. The _____ surface of an epithelial cell is opposite the apical surface

13. Second type of epithelial tissue; Makes up secreting portion of glands

14. Production and release of substances (e.g., sweat)

15. _____ and lining epithelium is one of two types of epithelial tissue

17. _____ membrane consists of the basal lamina and reticular lamina

19. This surface of an epithelial cell faces the adjacent cells on either side

20. Also known as epithelial tissue

23. Consists of a single cell or group that secrete substances into ducts, onto a surface or into blood

Epithelial Tissue

Dr. Evelyn J. Biluk

Word bank

ABSORPTION   APICAL   AVASCULAR   BASAL   BASEMENT   COLUMNAR   COVERING   CUBOIDAL   ENDOCRINE   ENDOTHELIUM   EPITHELIUM   EXOCRINE   GLAND   GLANDULAR   GOBLET   KERATIN   LATERAL   MESOTHELIUM   MICROVILLI   PAP   PSEUDOSTRATIFIED   SECRETION   SIMPLE   SQUAMOUS   STRATIFIED   TRANSITIONAL

Epithelial Tissue

Dr. Evelyn J. Biluk

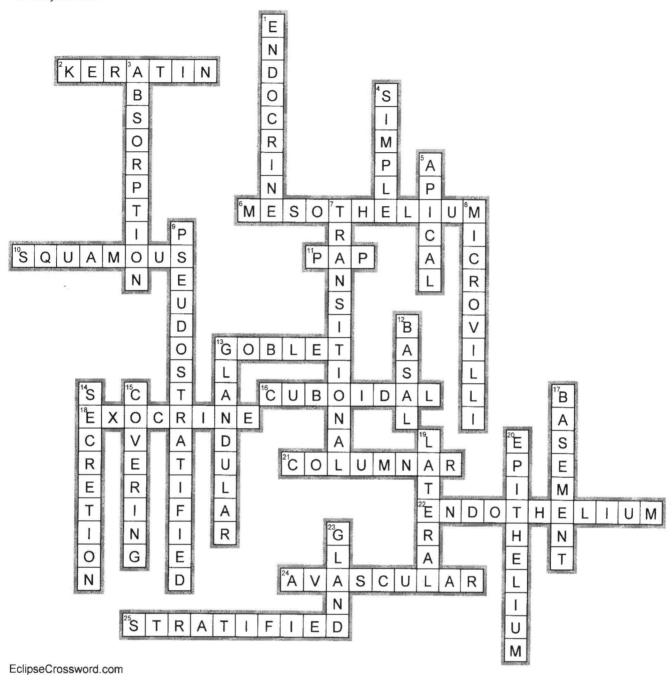

Connective Tissue

Dr. Evelyn J. Biluk

Connective Tissue

Dr. Evelyn J. Biluk

Across

2. Cells that transport oxygen to cells and remove carbon dioxide from them

5. Also known as fat cells or adipose cells

7. _____ connective tissue includes dense regular, dense irregular and elastic connective tissues

9. _____ fibers consist of collagen arrange in fine bundles; Provide support and strength

10. This classification of connnective tissue includes mesenchyme and mucous connective tissue

12. Cells involved in phagocytosis, immunity and allergic reactions

14. Procedure that involves the suctioning of small amounts of adipose tissue

17. _____ connective tissue includes blood tissue and lymph

20. Spaces within cartilage that house chrondrocytes

22. _____ connective tissue includes areolar, adipose and reticular connective tissues

23. Type of white blood cell that is derived from monocytes

24. Slippery substance that binds cells together, lubricates joints and maintains the shape of eyeballs

25. Small cells that develop from a B lymphocyte; Secrete antibodies

26. This classification of connective tissue includes structures like the scapula, femur, radius and ulna

27. These cells produce histamine; Also bind to, ingest and kill bacteria

29. Second type of bone tissue; Consists of trabeculae

30. Found between the cells and fibers of connective tissue

31. _____ fibers are strong and resist pulling forces; Allow tissue flexibility

32. This classification of connective tissue includes loose and dense connective tissue

33. _____ tissue is one of the most abundant tissues in the human body

Down

1. Large flat cells with branching processes; Most numerous cell found in connective tissue

3. _____ fibers made from protein elastin; Add strength and stability to connective tissue; Ability to return to original shape after being stretched

4. One type of bone tissue; Basic unit is called an osteon or Haversian system

6. Cells of mature cartilage

8. Connective tissue is composed of cells and _____

11. Also known as GAGs; Trap water making ground substance jellylike

13. Also known as WBCs; Not found in large numbers in normal connective tissue

15. Cell fragments that participate in blood clotting

16. Main adhesion protein of connective tissue

18. Extracellular fluid that flows in lymphatic vessels

19. Consists of core protein and GAGs

21. Provides support and adhesiveness in cartilage, bone, skin and blood vessels

28. This classification of connective tissue includes hyaline cartilage, fibrocartilage and elastic cartilage

Connective Tissue

Dr. Evelyn J. Biluk

Word bank

ADIPOCYTES   BONE   CARTILAGE   CHONDROITINSULFATE   CHRONDROCYTES   COLLAGEN

COMPACT   CONNECTIVE   DENSE   ELASTIC   EMBRYONIC   EXTRACELLULARMATRIX

FIBROBLASTS   FIBRONECTIN   GLYCOSAMINOGLYCANS   GROUNDSUBSTANCE   HYALURONICACID

LACUNAE   LEUKOCYTES   LIPOSUCTION   LIQUID   LOOSE   LYMPH   MACROPHAGES

MASTCELLS   MATURE   PLASMACELLS   PLATELETS   PROTEOGLYCANS   REDBLOODCELLS

RETICULAR   SPONGY   WHITEBLOODCELLS

Connective Tissue

Dr. Evelyn J. Biluk

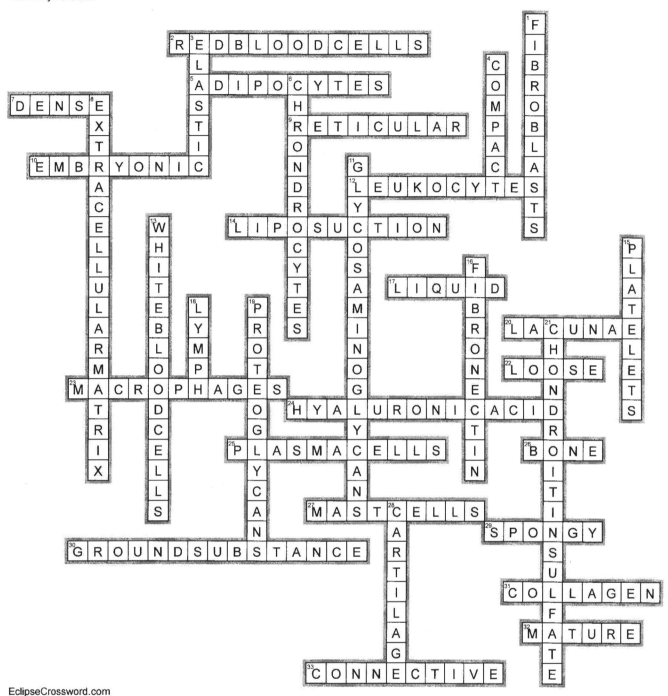

Muscular Tissue and Nervous Tissue

Dr. Evelyn J. Biluk

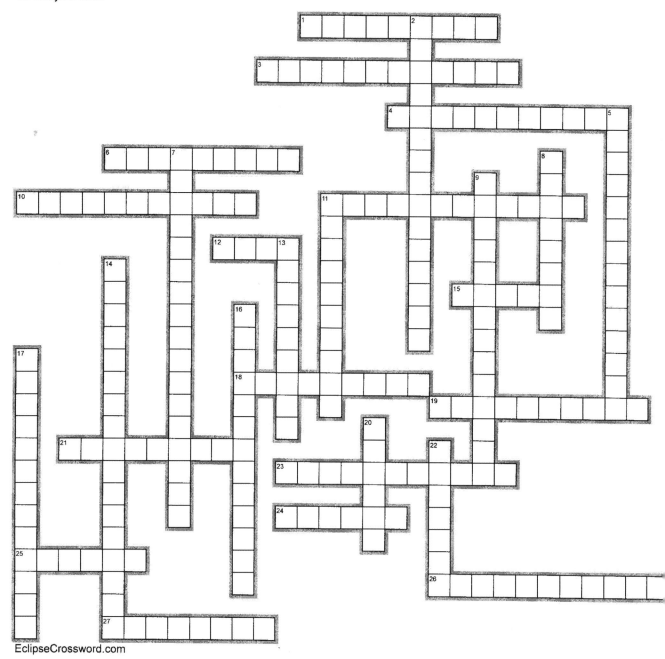

Muscular Tissue and Nervous Tissue

Dr. Evelyn J. Biluk

Across

1. When an action potential occurs in a muscle fiber, the muscle fiber _____

3. _____ are found in some smooth muscle tissues

4. Action potentials can propagate along the plasma membrane of a neuron or muscle fiber due to the presence of voltage-gated _____

6. Neurons and muscle fibers are regarded as _____ cells because they exhibit electrical excitability

10. Muscle contraction that is not consciously controlled

11. A _____ fiber is tapered at each end and thick in the middle

12. A single thin cylindrical process extending from the cell body; Output portion of a neuron

15. The function of cardiac muscle tissue is to pump _____ to all parts of the body

18. The ability of muscle to contract and relax by conscious control

19. _____ and gap junctions are associated with cardiac muscle tissue

21. _____ are tapering, highly branched, short cell processes extending from the cell body

23. Lack striations

24. Also known as a nerve cell

25. A third type of muscular tissue; Found in walls of hollow internal structures (e.g. blood vessels, airways)

26. Skeletal muscle is _____ in shape

27. This type of muscle tissue is attached to the bones of the human skeleton

14. Neurons release chemicals called _____

16. Nervous tissue is found in the _____

17. _____ consists of neurons and neuroglia

20. The function of smooth muscle tissue is _____ (e.g. propulsion of foods, contraction of bladder, constriction of blood vessels)

22. _____ muscle tissue is a second type; Found in the heart wall only

Down

2. Also known as a nerve impulse; Electrical signals sent to other neurons, muscle tissue or glands

5. The functions of _____ include motion, posture, heat production and protection

7. Thickenings of the plasma membrane of cardiac muscle fibers that contain desmosomes and gap junctions

8. The _____ of a neuron contains the nucleus and organelles

9. _____ consists of muscle fibers

11. Alternating dark and light bands found within muscle fibers of skeletal muscle

13. Cells that support neurons; Do not generate or conduct nerve impulses

Muscular Tissue and Nervous Tissue

Dr. Evelyn J. Biluk

Word bank

ACTIONPOTENTIAL   AXON   BLOOD   CARDIAC   CELLBODY   CONTRACTS   CYLINDRICAL
DENDRITES   DESMOSOMES   EXCITABLE   GAPJUNCTIONS   INTERCALATEDDISCS   INVOLUNTARY
IONCHANNELS   MOTION   MUSCULARTISSUE   NERVOUSSYSTEM   NERVOUSTISSUE   NEUROGLIA
NEURON   NEUROTRANSMITTERS   NONSTRIATED   SKELETAL   SKELETALMUSCLE   SMOOTH
SMOOTHMUSCLE   STRIATIONS   VOLUNTARY

Muscular Tissue and Nervous Tissue

Dr. Evelyn J. Biluk

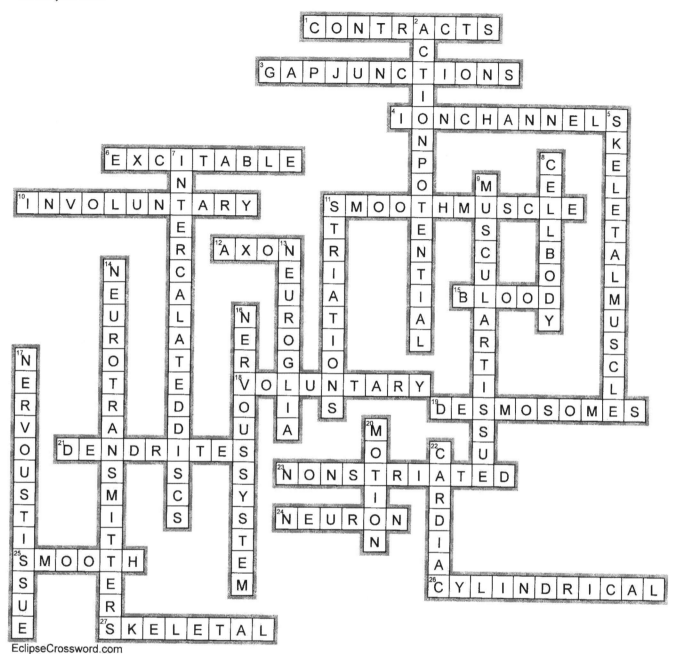

EclipseCrossword.com

Membranes

Dr. Evelyn J. Biluk

Membranes

Dr. Evelyn J. Biluk

Across

1. _____ membrane is third type of epithelial membrane; Also known as the skin

3. _____ membrane is a second type of membrane; Lines joints and contains connective tissue only

6. _____ cells secrete mucus; Found in epithelial layer of a mucous membrane

9. _____ membrane is a type of epithelial membrane; Also known as mucosa

12. _____ layer is part of the serous membrane; Covers and adheres to organs within the cavity

15. Layer attached to and lines the heart wall in the thoracic cavity

17. Serous membrane lining the thoracic cavity and covering the lungs

18. Mucous membranes line the digestive, respiratory and _____ tracts

19. Serous membranes do not open directly to the exterior of the body; Covers the organs that lie within the cavity

20. Layer below epidermis; Consists of areolar connective tissue and dense irregular connective tissue

21. Serous membrane lining the heart cavity and covering the heart

23. A watery lubricant from the mesothelium of a serous membrane; Allows organs to glide over one another easily

24. Simple squamous epithelium associated with serous membranes

25. The cavity between the parietal pericardium and visceral pericardium

13. _____ layer of the serous membrane is attached to and lines the cavity wall

14. Serous membrane lining the abdominal cavity and covering the abdominal organs

16. The cavity between the parietal pleura and visceral pleura

19. _____ membrane is one type of membrane; Combination of an epithelial layer and connective tissue layer

22. _____ membrane is a type of epithelial membrane; Also known as serosa

Down

2. _____ lubricates and nourishes cartilage covering bones and contains macrophages

3. Discontinuous layer of cells making up synovial membranes; Some secrete synovial fluid

4. Layer attached to and lining the thoracic cavity wall

5. Serous membranes have _____ layers

7. Connective tissue layer of a mucous membrane; Composed of areolar connective tissue

8. Layer that covers and adheres to the lungs

9. Flat sheets of pliable tisssue that either cover or line a part of the human body

10. Superficial portion of the skin

11. Layer that covers and adheres to the heart; Part of the heart

Membranes

Dr. Evelyn J. Biluk

Word bank

CUTANEOUS   DERMIS   EPIDERMIS   EPITHELIAL   EXTERIOR   GOBLET   LAMINAPROPRIA

MEMBRANES   MESOTHELIUM   MUCOUS   PARIETAL   PARIETALPERICARDIUM   PARIETALPLEURA

PERICARDIALCAVITY   PERICARDIUM   PERITONEUM   PLEURA   PLEURALCAVITY   REPRODUCTIVE

SEROUS   SEROUSFLUID   SYNOVIAL   SYNOVIALFLUID   SYNOVIOCYTES   TWO   VISCERAL

VISCERALPERICARDIUM   VISCERALPLEURA

Membranes
Dr. Evelyn J. Biluk

Epidermis and Dermis

Dr. Evelyn J. Biluk

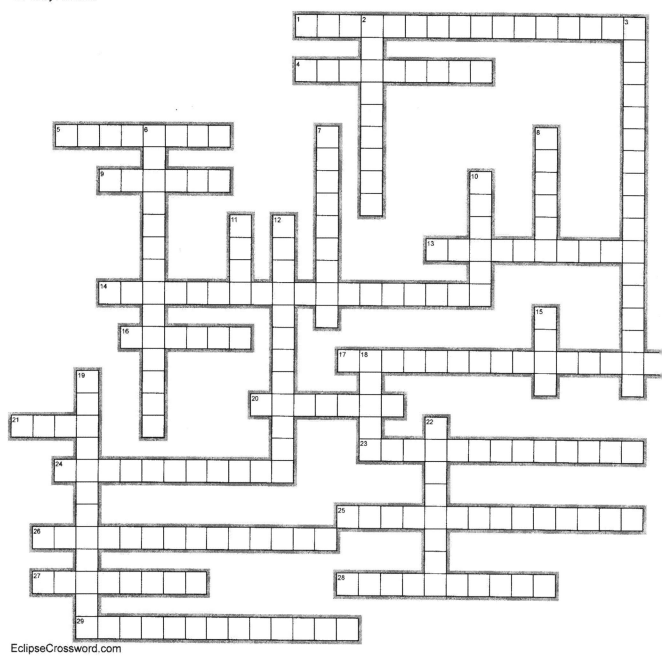

Epidermis and Dermis

Dr. Evelyn J. Biluk

Across

1. _____ give rise to the sensations of warmth, coolness, pain, tickle and itch

4. The _____ region is the deeper portion of the dermis; Consists of dense irregular connective tissue with collagen and elastic fibers

5. The accumulation of melanin in patches

9. Also known as stretch marks; Red or silvery white streaks on the surface of the skin

13. Oxygen carrying pigment that adds pink to red to skin color

14. Also known as the corpuscles of touch

16. Permanent coloration of the skin in which a foreign pigment is deposited into the dermis using a needle

17. Superficial layer to the stratum basale; Contains keratinocytes

20. Pigment that contributes to skin color and absorbs UV light

21. Also known as cutaneous membrane or integument

23. Cells arranged in 4 or 5 layers that make keratin

24. Cells that produce melanin

25. Layer of flattened, dead keratinocytes

26. Layer found only in thick skin (e.g. fingertips, palms)

27. An excessive amount of keratinized cells shed from the skin of the scalp

28. _____ cells participate in immune responses against microbes; Arise from red bone marrow and migrate to the epidermis

29. The deepest layer of the epidermis

15. _____ skin contains only 4 layers of epidermis

18. _____ skin contains 5 layers of epidermis

19. Formed by the combination of sweat and epidermal ridges touching a smooth object

22. Pigment that adds yellow to orange tint to skin; Found in carrots

Down

2. Superficial, thin part of the skin

3. Middle layer of the epidermis; Contains keratinocytes

6. The process of accumulating keratin as the cells move from one epidermal layer to the next

7. The _____ region is the most superficial portion of the dermis; Consists of areolar connective tissue with collagen and elastic fibers

8. _____ cells are the least numerous of the epidermal cells

10. Deeper, thicker part of the skin; Made up of connective tissue

11. A benign localized overgrowth of melanocytes

12. Also known as the subQ layer or hypodermis

Epidermis and Dermis

Dr. Evelyn J. Biluk

Word bank

CAROTENE   DANDRUFF   DERMIS   EPIDERMIS   FINGERPRINTS   FRECKLES   FREENERVEENDINGS

HEMOGLOBIN   KERATINIZATION   KERATINOCYTES   LANGERHANS   MEISSNERCORPUSCLES

MELANIN   MELANOCYTES   MERKEL   MOLE   PAPILLARY   RETICULAR   SKIN   STRATUMBASALE

STRATUMCORNEUM   STRATUMGRANULOSUM   STRATUMLUCIDUM   STRATUMSPINOSUM   STRIAE

SUBCUTANEOUS   TATTOO   THICK   THIN

Epidermis and Dermis

Dr. Evelyn J. Biluk

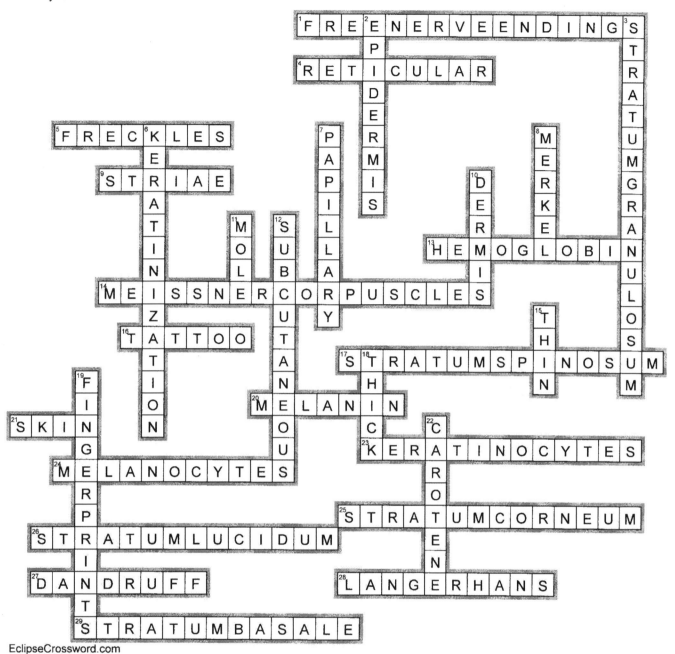

EclipseCrossword.com

Accessory Structures of Skin

Dr. Evelyn J. Biluk

Accessory Structures of Skin

Dr. Evelyn J. Biluk

Across

2. Excessive body hair disorder

7. _____ perspiration is sweat observed as moisture on the skin

8. Oil, sweat and ceruminous glands are of this type

9. Also known as nail plate; Visible part of nail

10. Inflammation of sebaceous glands

12. Columns of dead, keratinized epidermal cells; Bonded together with proteins

14. Structure surrounding the root of the hair

15. Also known as ear wax; Secreted by ceruminous glands; Impedes the entrances of insects and foreign substances into the ear

17. These glands are found in the external ear

18. Very fine, nonpigmented hairs that cover the fetal body

21. White crescent shaped area of proximal end of nail body

22. Portion of hair that penetrates into the dermis

24. _____ hair contains few melanin granules

25. Partial or complete lack of hair

26. These specialized glands found in the skin secrete milk

27. Hard, dead keratinized epidermal cells found on the surface of the distal part of the digits (hands and feet)

29. Also known as the cuticle

30. Substance secreted by sebaceous glands

31. These cells produce melanin; Give color to hair

32. _____ hairs are also known as "peach fuzz"; Short, fine pale hairs; Barely visible

16. _____ sweating occurs during fear or embarrassment

19. Muscles that contracts and can pull on a hair shaft; Stimulated by physiological or emotional stress

20. Also known as nail bed; Secures the nail to the fingertip

23. _____ hairs are long, coarse, heavily pigmented hairs (e.g., eyebrows, eyelashes, scalp)

28. _____ glands are also known as oil glands

Down

1. These sweat glands are also called merocrine sweat glands; More common than other type; Distributed in most regions of the body

3. _____ perspiration is sweat that evaporates from the skin before it is perceived as moisture

4. _____ hair lacks melanin; Accumulation of air bubbles in the shaft

5. _____ glands are also known as sudoriferous glands

6. _____ sweat glands are found mainly in the armpit, groin, areolae and face beards (males)

11. Process that adds or removes pigment to hair

13. Superficial part of hair; Projects above the skin's surface

Accessory Structures of Skin

Dr. Evelyn J. Biluk

Word bank

ACNE   ALOPECIA   APOCRINE   ARRECTORPILI   CERUMEN   CERUMINOUS   ECCRINE
EMOTIONAL   EPONYCHIUM   EXOCRINE   GRAY   HAIR   HAIRCOLORING   HAIRFOLLICLE
HIRUSUTISM   HYPONYCHIUM   INSENSIBLE   LANUGO   LUNULA   MAMMARY   MELANOCYTES
NAILBODY   NAILS   ROOT   SEBACEOUS   SEBUM   SENSIBLE   SHAFT   SWEAT   TERMINAL
VELLUS   WHITE

Accessory Structures of Skin

Dr. Evelyn J. Biluk

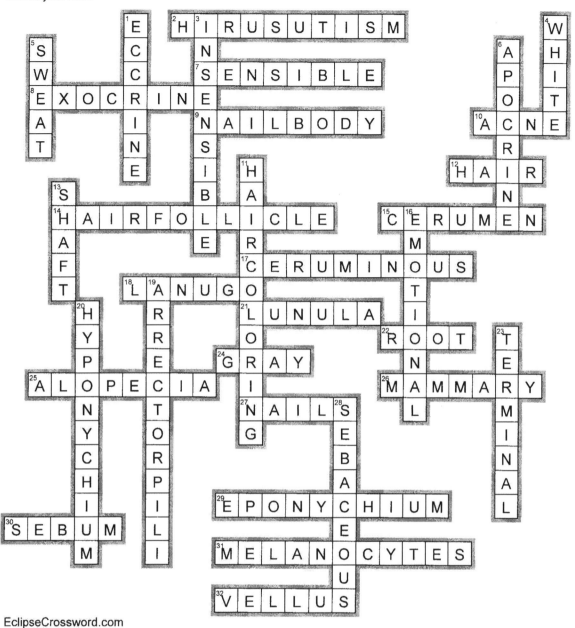

EclipseCrossword.com

Made in the USA
San Bernardino, CA
24 May 2020